It's another Quality Book from CGP

This book is for anyone doing GCSE English
or GCSE English Language and Literature.

It contains lots of tricky questions designed
to make you sweat — because that's the only
way you'll get any better.

It's also got some daft bits in to try and make
the whole experience at least vaguely
entertaining for you.

What CGP is all about

Our sole aim here at CGP is to produce the highest quality
books — carefully written, immaculately presented and
dangerously close to being funny.

Then we work our socks off to get them out to you
— at the cheapest possible prices.

CONTENTS

Section Five — Writing About Prose, Drama and Poetry

Section Six — Language and Grammar

Section Seven — Spoken Language Study

Published by CGP

Editors:
Rachael Powers
Caley Simpson
Hayley Thompson
Karen Wells

Contributors:
Elspeth Bain
Shona McIntosh
Victoria Morgan

With thanks to Lorraine Campbell and Luke von Kotze for the proofreading.

ISBN: 978 1 84146 102 1

Clipart from Corel®
Printed by Elanders Ltd, Newcastle upon Tyne.

Based on the classic CGP style created by Richard Parsons.

Planning and Introductions

Q1 Turn the points under the question below into an essay plan by sorting them out under the headings **Introduction**, **Development** and **Conclusion**.

> *Many scientists think human activities are contributing to climate change.*
> *Write an article for a magazine persuading people to live a greener lifestyle.*

- Too much 'leisure' time spent sitting behind computers or watching TV — too little exercise = increased risk of heart disease, and constant use of electricity causing pollution.

  Spend less time watching TV/using computers — do a bit more exercise for fun.

- Need to change the way we live.

- It's possible to change the way we live by choosing more carefully what we eat, and by being more active. This will make our lifestyles much healthier, and be far better for the environment.

- Driving cars — not enough exercise, using up the world's oil and creating pollution.

  Can use public transport or even better cycle or walk to work or shops.

- Way we live not just unhealthy for us — not good for the environment either.

- Busy work schedules mean less time to prepare proper food.

  Convenience foods don't have enough nutrients in them for a healthy balanced diet. Also convenience foods have more packaging — creates more rubbish.

  We can take time to prepare fresh food — healthier diet and less rubbish.

Q2 This introduction rambles on without making a clear point.
Write it out again and underline everything that shouldn't be in an introduction.

> **Modern lifestyles are becoming more unhealthy, and this is something which my Mum has been saying for ages. When I was in the shower last week, she said that I had been wasting loads of hot water. There is an increased risk of heart disease due to lack of exercise, and general ill health caused by poor eating habits. We can choose to walk or cycle to the shops or to work, instead of using up the world's natural resources. Increasingly, the way we live our daily lives needs to change, if we are to stop the damage we are doing to ourselves and the world around us.**

Q3 Look at the question below. There are loads of different ways you could introduce your answer. Write three brief introductions, following the instructions in a) to c).

> *Many scientists think human activities are contributing to climate change.*
> *Write an article for a magazine persuading people to live a greener lifestyle.*

a) Rephrase the wording of the question.

b) Be imaginative.

c) Define a key term in the question.

Paragraphs

Q1   There are five good reasons for starting a new paragraph in the box.
Write down the reason for the paragraph change in each of these pieces of writing.

There may be more than one reason.

> new person   new time   new place   new person speaking   new topic

a)   The rain poured down onto the busy street as Mr. Sanders picked his way through noisy street-sellers, filthy children and stray dogs. The whole city seemed intent on keeping him from his appointment.

At High Court House, Miss Loxham was impatiently awaiting the arrival of her tutor.

b)   "If we hide in the hedge he'll never find us," hissed Susan, as they sprinted across the field, away from the old man's house.

"But I don't think we can make it before he sees us," replied Danny, between breaths. He gave her a frightened look and they increased their pace, adrenaline flowing through their veins.

c)   Osteoarthritis is now easily treated by a hip replacement operation. This operation is a great success story for medical science. Although quite a complicated procedure, there's an almost 100% success rate in patients.

However, rheumatoid arthritis is far less easy to treat. As yet, there is no known method of ridding patients of the disease, although it can be controlled by drugs.

d)   Mrs Jain commented that the play was a triumph. The actors were excellent and the performance and comic timing were extremely slick.

Miss Booth, on the other hand, felt that the casting of 'Roxy' was unwise, as she tended to dominate the stage and stifle the other characters' performances.

Q2   These paragraphs sound very disjointed. Use linking words to make them flow more smoothly. Reword the first sentence of the second paragraph of each extract.

a)   I couldn't understand what had possessed Arthur to paint his living room lime green. It looked horrendous and it took all my powers of pretence to congratulate him on the new look.

There's no accounting for taste and perhaps in five years' time it will be the height of fashion and everyone will have lime green walls.

b)   In the present day we crave material goods above everything else. You only need to look at the millions of people across the country who enter the lottery each week, hoping to boost their spending powers.

People are working longer hours and taking less holiday. It's not healthy and it's becoming clear that we need to readdress our priorities in life.

c)   Mountain climbing is a potentially dangerous sport. Every year people die in their pursuit of reaching the summit, but this doesn't put others off.

It is necessary to prepare carefully for a mountain expedition. You need to take lots of different equipment to cover a large number of eventualities.

Paragraphs

Q1   These paragraphs are in the wrong order. Reorder them to make the extracts clear and logical.

a)   "We understand a substantial proportion of the new notes are still in bank or Post Office branches and have not been issued to the general public," said a Bank of England spokesman.
        The Bank of England has made an embarrassing discovery. It has had to halt distribution of the new £5 note after it was discovered parts of the note's design were disappearing.
        The Bank stated that about 10 million of the new £5 notes had been distributed. The new note is the same size and colour as the old fiver.

b)   Increased emissions of methane are also contributing to the greenhouse effect, although on a far smaller scale than carbon dioxide. One reason for the increased emissions is the modern practice of intensive animal farming.
        Carbon dioxide emissions are largely caused by extensive deforestation and fossil-fuel burning — both of which are common in society today.
        Global warming is a natural process but human activity is speeding it up. The most significant factor contributing to global warming is increased emissions of carbon dioxide, the main greenhouse gas.

Q2   Write a separate paragraph for each bullet point.

a)   • We eat too much junk food
        • We don't take enough exercise
        • On average people are getting fatter and unhealthier
        • Need to change lifestyle

b)   • Selina arrived at her new school
            • No one spoke to her all morning
            • Jo started chatting to Selina at lunchtime
            • She felt much happier

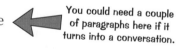

You could need a couple of paragraphs here if it turns into a conversation.

Q3   What do you think it is about the paragraphs below that makes them interesting?

a) _"So let's work with our teachers, not against them. Let's work together to put these plans in action. Don't ask what your school can do for you: ask what you can do for your school."_

b) _"Do we really want to lose this beautiful area of idyllic countryside? Are we honestly prepared to sit back and do nothing while bulldozers rip up trees and grassland and this haven for local wildlife is concreted over?"_

Formal and Informal Language

Q1   Write your own (brief) definition of formal language.

Q2   For each of the tasks below, say whether you would use formal or informal language.

   a) Writing a letter of complaint to your local council about litter and graffiti in your area.

   b) Giving a talk to primary school children about the benefits of eating healthily.

   c) Writing an article for a website aimed at teenagers, advising them what to do if they're being bullied.

   d) Making a speech to the school governors, asking them to get rid of your school uniform.

   e) Writing a letter of application for a summer job at a sports centre.

Q3   Rewrite these paragraphs in formal essay-style English.

   • **NO** slang
   • **NO** clichés.
   • **NO** vague words.
   • **DON'T** say 'I'.

   a) *I reckon Shakespeare makes Oberon and Titania have a go at each other because he wants to point out the difference between people who just get things sorted and know the score, and people who just run about falling in and out of love all of the time.*

   b) By writing about that Willy Loman bloke, Arthur Miller makes us think about the way we treat every Joe Bloggs in the street. I feel well sorry for him.

   c) *All that snow and white stuff makes you think of winter. I think the weather shows how the poet is feeling as well, because she must be lonely and bored being indoors all the time. This first bit of the poem sort of makes you think this for the rest of the poem, too.*

   d) Shakespeare is having a go at us for fancying people just because of what they look like. We can see this when he makes Demitrius dump Helena the first time around because he thinks she's really ugly.

Q4   You don't always have to write in formal language. Sometimes you're tested on how well you can write in other styles. Rewrite the paragraph below in tabloid newspaper style.

> Scientists have long believed that many of the cures to modern diseases are to be found under the sea, and recent studies in the pharmaceutical industry have suggested that there could also be a marine-based substance that can radically alter the signs of aging. The chemical, which is present in a rare type of coral, is said to improve the elasticity of the epidermis by 98 per cent when taken internally in tablet form. This new study has produced an uproar among environmentalists, who claim the activities of the profit-driven pharmaceutical industry pose a serious threat to the coral, which is a protected species.

Giving Evidence and Quoting

Q1 Write out the paragraphs below, then underline the evidence backing up the statement alongside.

a) After running about in the garden all day, Felix finally came indoors to eat his food. When Katy bent down to pat him, she noticed pieces of red cloth sticking out from between his teeth which matched the colour of Pete's slippers. Felix ate all of his food happily.

Felix chewed Pete's slippers.

b) Patricia looked fantastic as she pulled up in her shiny new sports car. It was a beautiful day, and her neighbour Daniel was outside doing some gardening when she emerged from the car, shouting over to him, 'Hey, Dan, what do you think of my new car?' At that moment, Daniel turned on his lawn mower and pretended not to have heard her.

Daniel was jealous of Patricia's new car.

c) The wind was blowing hard and Skipper Johnson had a bad feeling in his stomach. The colour of the sky didn't look good to him. He knew he had to tell the others that it might come to the point of abandoning ship within an hour, as he watched the waves crashing over the deck.

Skipper Johnson knew there was danger ahead.

Q2 Write out the sentences below, putting in quotation marks where you think there is a direct quote.

a) Mrs. Wittaker said, If I don't get the children vaccinated, I could be putting their lives in danger. There are plenty of parents like Mrs. Wittaker who feel the same way.

b) There can be no excuses for children who do not get their homework in on time. I am prepared to stay behind after school to supervise detentions. Mr. Snodgrass, the chemistry teacher, had to make this clear after receiving only four homework books last Tuesday.

Q3 Now rewrite the sentences from Q2 in such a way that you don't need speech marks.

Make sure you don't change the meaning of the original.

Q4 The paragraphs below don't make much sense — the quotes are in the wrong place. Rewrite the paragraphs, rearranging the sentences so the quotes are in the right place.

a) "We're getting better after each game," the team's manager said yesterday. There have been frequent criticisms of the country's leading football team recently, despite the fact that they are still at the top of the premier division. However, other pundits have put the recent wave of criticism down to jealousy of the team's success, and point out that it has certainly not altered their performance at all. This comes after a remark made by a major sports journalist who described them on prime time television as being "dirty players with no real tactics."

b) When asked how she felt about having such a flower named after her, Suzie Starlet gushed simply, "I'm flattered and honoured." A flower show spokesperson described the now famous flower as "a beautiful pink and orange rose with a delicate perfume." A new flower has been named after the glamorous film actress, Suzie Starlet. The flower, now to be known as a 'Pink Suzie' was unveiled yesterday by its famous namesake at the annual flower show in Brighton.

Writing Conclusions

Q1 Put sentences a) to d) in order so that they form a conclusion to the question below.

*Does anything actually happen in the play to change the
way we perceive the fate of its main characters?*

a) The writer creates a perpetual cycle of anticipation and boredom throughout the play which comes to represent the human condition.

b) The mere promise of change gives the play momentum, but the fate of the main characters does not change, nor does our perception of it.

c) Estragon and Vladimir have episodes of activity throughout the play, and there are moments when it seems as though something will happen, or that the scene will change dramatically.

d) There can be no dispute that at the end of the play, we are left with the feeling that nothing significant has really changed.

Q2 For each of the following, write down whether it's a conclusion 'do' or a conclusion 'don't'.

a) Beginning with the phrase 'In conclusion...'.

b) Summarising your main ideas.

c) Referring to a point you made in your introduction.

d) Referring to the original question.

e) Introducing a new piece of evidence to finalise your argument.

f) Discussing the implications of your conclusion.

Q3 Write the conclusion for an essay on the question below, using the information in the box.

What is the main difference between people who dance and those who don't?

- There seems to be a great division between people who like to dance and those who don't.

- The ability to really let yourself go on the dance floor comes down to a question of confidence. Those who don't have any difficulty dancing wildly in front of others always seem to be the centre of attention in other areas of their lives. Those who seem to lack confidence in general tend to lurk in the shadows at discos, pretending not to want to dance, when really they do.

- Confidence is not something we are simply born with, it can also be learned. A recent study carried out in California showed that 8 people in every 10 who were questioned regarded themselves as 'not that confident really,' but when asked to perform circus tricks in front of a live audience, they were all successful in completing the task. So the main division between those who dance and those who don't seems to be a matter of choice as much as anything.

Essays, schmessays — I'd like to see the examiners write some...

Conclusions are easy to muck up in an exam — especially when you don't leave enough time to write one. So keep half an eye on that clock all the way through.

Reading the Text and Making Notes

Q1 You need to know what to look for when reading non-fiction texts.
Underline the key words in the example questions below.

a) What do you learn about the thoughts and feelings of the writer in 'A better future for our children?'

b) How does the image and headline of 'I Wish I'd Never...' add to the effectiveness of the text?

c) Compare how the writers use language to achieve their purpose in 'Paradise Lost: the corruption of one of the most beautiful places on earth' and 'Amazing Island Experiences'.

Q2 Find an article from a newspaper or magazine. It can be on any topic, but most paragraphs should have more than two sentences, and it should be at least seven paragraphs long.
Cut it out and stick it onto a plain piece of paper to give you space for note making.

a) Sum up the central idea of the article in one sentence.
Write it near the top of your page.

b) On the article itself and on the plain sheet of backing paper, underline key words and make notes to show how the writer has organised their ideas. You might want to pick out key points, comment on the language, comment on the tone, look for any use of humour and comment on any headlines or graphics.

Q3 Have a look at this exam question and the article that goes with it. Underline and make notes on the points of the article that are relevant to the question.

What do you learn from the article about Katie Atkins' job?
How does the writer use language to express her opinions?

NEW START FOR OLD CLOTHES

When Katie Atkins wanted to make a bit of extra cash, she didn't go for the usual part-time jobs such as waitressing or babysitting. Oh no. Creative Katie, 16, decided to make the most of her talent with textiles and start making new clothes out of old. She raided her wardrobe, her mum's and her sister's, and got hold of unwanted, unworn or damaged clothes. Then, armed with just some scissors and a sewing kit, she set about revamping the tired old clothes and turning them into something desirable.

"It just started out as a bit of fun," says Katie. "But then I saw how much people like them, and Mum suggested I start selling them." Katie sells her clothes mainly at craft fairs, but you can look at her designs on her website (www.katiesclothes.co.uk), and even commission an item just for you.

Writing Your Answer

Q1 Read the following article and summarise the key points.
Make sure you don't just copy out bits of the text though.

> For Jonathan Higgins, owning a dog isn't just for fun. Jonathan breeds championship poodles, and has won prizes at dog shows all over the country. His newest poodle, Harold Henry Huntingdon III is tipped to take the top prize at a number of upcoming shows.
>
> Jonathan puts his success down to three things: dedication, attention to detail and a genuine love of poodles. "Some people think poodles are a bit silly," he says. "But I think they're fascinating —they're really intelligent, and you can train them to do all sorts of things. Plus, it's fun to clip their fur into different shapes."

Q2 Look at the question and decide which opening line is better. Write down why.

Explain how the letter from the charity tries to persuade people to donate money.

a)
> The Charity letter uses short paragraphs to make its ideas easy to understand and therefore likely to persuade people to give money, but it also explains in detail how the money will be spent and gives a case study to show what a difference a small donation can make.

b)
> The Charity letter is trying to persuade people to give money to a good cause.

Q3 Match the statements below to the piece of evidence that backs them up.

a) It's much easier to quit smoking if you use a nicotine patch.

b) Romantic comedies are the best type of film.

c) Most people aren't eating the recommended amount of fruit and veg each day.

In a survey, 7 out of 10 adults said they were eating fewer than 5 pieces of fruit and veg a day.

In a survey of teenage girls, 3 in 4 said that romantic comedies were their favourite type of film

In a survey of people who used to smoke, 80% of them said nicotine patches helped them to quit.

After the film's premiere the romantic comedy 'The Mystery Engagement' received positive reviews.

A survey found that apples were the most popular lunchbox snack.

80% of smokers said they would consider using nicotine patches if they decided to quit smoking.

Writing Your Answer

Q1 Read the following article and answer the questions below.

YOUR MONEY OR YOUR LIFE

You can't go shopping nowadays without bumping into at least two well-meaning people with buckets asking you to donate money to help provide clean water/wheelchairs/shelter (delete as appropriate). Don't get me wrong, each one is undeniably a good cause. But I'd rather help out in a different way than just by throwing a few quid into a bucket out of guilt.

No, I'd prefer to actually *do* something — volunteer at a homeless shelter or take under-privileged children on trips. It's a much better feeling, knowing that you've brightened someone's day, than feeling smug because you opened your purse. I reckon if a few more of the bucket-people spent some time with the people they're trying to help, everyone would get a lot more out of it. And I'd be able to get my shopping done in peace.

a) What do you think the author's attitude to charity is?

b) What does the writer suggest people should do to help out?

c) How does the writer use language to get their point across?

Q2 Which of the following should you try and work out when reading non-fiction texts?

How long the article took to write.

What the writer had for tea.

What the writer's attitude is.

What the writer wants to make you feel.

How old the writer is.

Whether the writer's male or female.

When the article was written.

The purpose of the article.

Q3 Find two non-fiction texts on the same subject. Write two paragraphs in answer to this question.

Compare the two texts and explain which one you think is more successful. Think about any differences in audience and purpose as well as similarities and differences between the texts themselves.

E.g. an encyclopaedia entry on a castle or cathedral and a tourist leaflet on the same place.

Writing About the Format of a Media Text

Q1 Find an example of a media text that is aimed at young people and one which is aimed at an older and more professional audience. Make a list of the differences between them.

Q2 Look at these headlines. Decide whether each one uses humour, exaggeration or shocking facts.

a) **Truancy levels set to hit 50%**

b) **Government dragging country into ruin**

c) **Small cemetery causes grave problem**

d) **Celebrity confession sparks mass outrage**

e) **1 in 10 primary school children obese**

Q3 Write a paragraph about the layout and format of this book. Write about:

- the font
- the layout
- the use of pictures

Bad one liners make perfect head-liners...
Most media texts are pretty devious. They want you to believe what they're saying, and they'll try anything to get you to believe it — from attention grabbing fonts to really bad jokes. Ahem.

Different Forms

Q1   Read the following letters and decide if each one is formal or informal.

a)
> 12th May 2010
>
> Dear Vicky,
>   Just wanted to tell you about this amazing film I saw last week. It was called 'Death on the River' and it's the scariest film I've ever seen! The acting is brilliant, and there's a twist at the end that I didn't see coming at all. I'd definitely recommend it.
> Love from,
> Sarah

b)
> 15th July 2010
>
> Dear Ms Wells,
>   I am writing to you to express my interest in the vacancy advertised in the Evening Times for the position of Accounts Manager. I have three years previous experience in a similar line of work, and I am hard-working, dedicated and a quick learner. Please find enclosed my CV. I look forward to hearing from you.
> Yours sincerely,
> Nick Wilson

Q2   Write a short article for a newspaper or magazine on a subject that interests you. Remember to include a headline and write in a journalistic style.

Q3   Copy out the text below, adding headings, subheadings, bullet points and any other appropriate layout features to turn it into a leaflet.

> Lancaster Zoo is a fantastic day out for all the family. It has many different species of animals, including lions, tigers, giraffes, elephants, rhinos and hippos. It's set in approximately 75 acres of land, and is open from 9am to 5pm April to October. It's easy to get to — just turn off the M6 at junction 33 and follow the elephant signs. There's plenty of parking and good wheelchair and pushchair access. Special attractions include our Underwater World; a glass tunnel underneath the shark enclosure; Up Close and Personal, where visitors can hand-feed a zebra; Bath Time — watch the elephants play in the mud and Monkey Land, where the monkeys swing from trees and ropes. The zoo is also proud of its conservation work; since opening in 1985, it has taken part in many different conservation projects around the world. Its rare-species breeding programmes are world-renowned, and last year Lancaster Zoo was proud to welcome the first snow leopard born in captivity in the UK. It's well worth a visit.

You don't need to worry about colouring in your leaflet or drawing pictures.

Q4   Write a speech for your school assembly on the sporting facilities available in your area, encouraging people to take part in more sports.

Audience

Q1   Match the following extracts with their intended audience.

Extract

a) *I am concerned about the terrible state of the local roads. There are an unacceptable number of potholes, which are not only dangerous but also cause damage to the vehicles which cannot avoid them.*

b) *I'm sure you'll agree that there just aren't enough things for teenagers to do in the evenings. Since the skate park was closed, we have nowhere to hang out and are reduced to spending our time on the streets.*

c) *I was disgusted with the service in your establishment. The waiters were rude, the food (when it eventually arrived) was overpriced and tasteless and the whole evening was very disappointing.*

d) *Is it right that the children of Norfolk Street Primary School have to cross a busy road to get into school? Your children's safety should be the school's priority and yet it refuses to provide a lollipop lady or an alternative.*

e) *Just pop over after school and we can work together on that project. If we get it finished in time, we could even go to the cinema afterwards.*

Audience

i)   A friend

ii) A local politician

iii) An adult audience

iv) A teenage audience

v)   A business manager

Q2   Imagine you're writing a letter to a friend. Sort these examples into DOs and DON'Ts.

It woz gr8 2 c u last nite.

It's always a pleasant surprise to find that your nice, free weekend has vanished into a pile of completely unnecessary homework.

Yours faithfully,
Lee Williams

Hi Pippa,
Hope you enjoyed your holiday.

It was really nice to see you at the weekend — I can't believe it's so long since we last met up. We definitely shouldn't leave it that long next time.

Can't wait to see you.

The beach is an area of outstanding natural beauty. The tourist will find themselves lost in the idyllic surroundings.

__Purpose__

Q1 Underline the words in the example questions below that indicate their purpose.

  a) Write a speech for a school council meeting persuading them that your school should set up an after-school trampolining club.

  b) Write a leaflet advising people on how to be more environmentally friendly.

  c) Write a letter to a local business persuading them to give you a job.

  d) Write a letter to a friend describing a scary experience.

Q2 Imagine you're the examiner. Write a question for each of the following purposes (the first one has been done for you as an example).

  a) informing   *Write a leaflet about your town, informing people about local attractions.*

  b) arguing

  c) describing

  d) explaining

  e) persuading

  f) advising

Imagine you're the examiner. Explain what made you choose that hat.

Q3 Read the question below. The first part of the answer has been written for you. Write a second paragraph that covers the second purpose of the article.

> *Write an article for a travel magazine informing people about the attractions in your area and persuading them to visit.*

> *Cornwall is full of exciting things to see and do. It has miles and miles of beautiful coastlines, pretty seaside towns like St Ives and St Just, and fascinating attractions like the Eden Project. While you're in Cornwall, why not go to Land's End, the most south-westerly point in Great Britain? For all you surfers out there, Cornwall has plenty of beaches and surf schools, catering for beginners to experts. There's also a huge range of wildlife, both flora and fauna.*

Arguing or Persuading

Q1   In each of the boxes there's a different version of a paragraph written in an argument essay.
       One uses evidence effectively and one just doesn't get it right.

a)   Which of these paragraphs uses facts without getting bogged down in them?

i)   Out of the sample questioned
      90% were in favour of the name
      change, while only one person
      out of every fifty thought the
      new name difficult to remember.

ii)   The vast majority of people are in
      favour of the change of name and
      also think the new name will be
      easy to remember.

b)   Which one of these paragraphs uses an expert opinion backed up with a quotation?

i)   Doctors are keen for people to
      improve their health by taking
      more exercise. A representative
      of the 'Fight that Fat Association'
      said, "Being overweight and a
      couch potato leads to many health
      problems and shortens life."

ii)   Lots of people feel that men
      and women should take
      more exercise. This would
      help with fitness.

c)   Which of these two paragraphs uses real-life examples to support what it says?

i)   High exam grades can be
      very useful. Getting a good
      GCSE grade in English can
      improve a student's future
      prospects.

ii)   Achieving a C or above in English
      gives 16-year-olds a much wider
      choice of courses in the sixth form or
      at college, and increases their chances
      of becoming high earners.

Q2   The paragraph in the box below is not very effective — it sounds vague, uncertain and weak.
       Rewrite it to sound more definite.

You can add a
few more lines if
you want to.

      I feel it might be a good idea to pay an official reward to successful
      GCSE students. Maybe it would encourage some to greater efforts.

Q3   Now develop the argument by writing another paragraph to follow
       on from your answer to Q2. Put forward logical reasons why
       paying GCSE candidates a reward will help them, their schools,
       and society in general.

You don't just have to use
facts well — you've got
to keep your argument
clear and logical too.

Arguing or Persuading

In order to make your writing effective when you're arguing or persuading don't forget these four tips:

1) Make a special point of being courteous and respectful to people with different opinions.

2) Use "we" and "you" to make your reader feel personally involved in what you are saying.

3) Rhetorical questions make people feel they already agree with you. Why not use them?

4) Say things in threes. It's powerful, forceful and punchy.

Q1 In the box below there is a very poor piece of argument writing. Rewrite it taking account of the four tips given above. You should be able to expand it into three or four paragraphs.

> Sixteen-year-olds should be given the vote and if you don't think so you're stupid. Lots of people agree with this idea and feel that sixteen- and seventeen-year-olds are often just as responsible and involved in their communities as older teenagers. After all, people can get married or join the army at 16.

Q2 Read these paragraphs. Write down which of the tips at the top of the page each one uses to make it convincing.

a) UHT milk is a foul-tasting product that should not be forced on anyone. I am, however, well aware that sincere and well-meaning people, no doubt including many of my readers, support its use on the grounds of convenience and cost.

b) I beg them to reconsider their position. We all want cheap, safe and convenient food. However, does that justify making people drink this stuff?

"Did someone say unnatural, unpalatable and disgusting?"

c) Is it right to expect people to drink something they dislike?

d) UHT milk is unnatural, unpalatable and disgusting. You can help to see it banished from every kitchen in the land.

Q3 Use the four tips to write a short response to someone who has said that all teenagers are lazy.

You could begin:

Mr Jones may have had unfortunate experiences with teenagers but he cannot fairly conclude that all teenagers are the same.

Think About Your Readers

Q1　The school fund-raising committee is drafting a letter for pupils to take home, asking for contributions to help fund a new school swimming pool. Use their notes to help you write three paragraphs for the letter.

Who are the readers?

- parents
- other close relatives of pupils

What will their worries and concerns be?

- pool needs to be built quickly if their child is to benefit from it
- people need to feel they are getting something for their money — maybe put names on tiles at the poolside for anyone contributing over £25

What will they say to argue against the idea?

- there is a public swimming pool only four miles away which the school has hired two mornings a week for years
- a swimming pool will be a dangerous hazard on a school site

Q2　Write an essay plan for this persuasive writing task.
Organise your planning notes under the same three headings used above.

Write an article for a local newspaper arguing that more money should be spent on libraries so they can improve internet access for all.

Q3　Write a plan for an advertising leaflet persuading people to take holidays in your local area. Organise your planning notes under the following three headings.

- _Who are the readers?_
- _What will they be interested in?_
- _Why should they take their holidays in your area?_

Q4　Look carefully at the notes you have made. Now choose either the task from Q2 or the task from Q3 and write the piece in full using your notes to help with planning.

Writing to Inform or Explain

Q1   For the example questions below, circle the key words — the purpose, audience and form.

a)   You are planning on starting a yoga class for students at your school. Write the text for a leaflet for
      pupils informing them about the class and persuading them to join.

b)   You went to see a film at the cinema recently. Write a review of the film for your school magazine
      to persuade your fellow students to go and see it.

c)   You have noticed a lot of litter in your local area. Write a letter to the council arguing that there
      should be more bins and recycling facilities.

d)   Your school is planning on twinning with a school in Spain. Write a speech to give to your class
      explaining what it will involve and arguing whether or not you think it's a good idea.

Q2   Write out these paragraphs in full by matching each opening statement to its evidence.

Opening Statements

a)   Boys are consistently out-performed by girls.

b)   Slouching can also lead to problems later in life.

c)   It was not just the final scoreline which indicated the better side.

d)   The city of Athens cut traffic volume with remarkable results.

e)   Children are getting fatter.

Evidence

i)   *A quick glance at all the statistics, from the amount of possession to the number of bookings
       shows that United were struggling that day.*

ii)   *Not only have exercise levels dropped in the last twenty-five years, but 87% of 13- to
       16-year-olds put TV viewing or playing computer games amongst their top three hobbies.*

iii)   *Almost overnight, levels of carbon monoxide halved.*

iv)   *56% of all back-pain sufferers in their fifties admit to having had poor posture as teenagers.*

v)   *For the fifth year in a row, their performance in exams, for the majority of subjects has been
       the weaker of the two sexes.*

Q3   Write a fact, statistic or example to back up the statements below.

a)   J. K. Rowling is a successful author.

b)   Exercise is good for you.

c)   Hugh Jackman is extremely good looking.

Writing to Inform or Explain

Q1 Have a look at the plan for the example question below.
Then write your own plan for the next question.

> Write an article for a magazine advising teenagers on how to eat healthily.

> Write a speech to give to primary school children explaining what secondary school is like.

This is the question you need to write your plan for.

PLAN
Purpose: to advise
Form: magazine article
Audience: teenagers
Points to include:
1) Eat lots of fruit and veg — 5 portions a day
2) Cut back on fatty, sugary and salty foods
3) Eat lots of fibre
4) Try to stick to a balanced diet

Q2 Copy out the text below adding headings and bullet points to make it suitable for a leaflet informing people how to make the most of the countryside.

> There are a few things you should remember for your own safety and to protect the countryside. To stay safe, always plan ahead. Check out things like weather and tides so you won't get caught out. Make sure you're dressed appropriately and have water, food, a first aid kit and a mobile phone in case you get into difficulties. Leave gates as you find them (they'll usually be closed, but sometimes they're left open). Keep your dogs under control and don't let them bother farm animals. Protect the countryside by not dropping any litter and not disturbing wildlife. Don't pick any plants. The countryside is a beautiful place — let's keep it that way.

Q3 For each sentence below, write another sentence that gives the same information without the personal tone. The first one is done for you as an example.

a) When I went to town on Saturday, I had to wait over half an hour for a bus.
People in the local community need more regular bus services.

b) I have noticed that there is more graffiti since the youth club was closed down.

c) I water my plant once a week, and re-pot it every six months.

d) Summers are hotter now than they were when I was young.

e) I think the council needs to sort out parking in town. My dad can never find anywhere to park.

Make Sure Everyone Can Understand

Q1   Look at the sentences below and underline the technical terms. The first one has been done for you.

   a)   At the brass band concert, the <u>flugelhorn</u> played a beautiful <u>solo</u>, showing off many techniques such as <u>vibrato</u> and <u>double-tonguing</u>.

   b)   Sauté the mushrooms and onions until soft. Add the liquid and simmer gently over a medium heat for 5 minutes.

   c)   To calculate the gradient of the line, you have to differentiate the original function.

   d)   Stephen's restart kick went out on the full, giving the opposition a scrum on the halfway line.

   e)   The suspension on my classic 1962 Jaguar E-Type had completely gone. The brakes and steering needed fixing too.

Q2   This passage is a bit vague. Rewrite it using some more facts and figures. It's OK just to make them up.

> In a survey of many people, most of them were in favour of the new statue for the town centre. Of the few who objected, their problems were of a financial nature, rather than disliking the original idea. Although this project would cost quite a lot, some of the money would be donated by the council, and the rest could be raised by fund-raising events.

Q3   Write a magazine article about something you're interested in. Assume that your audience doesn't know anything about the subject, so make sure you explain any technical terms you use.

Q4   Read this passage. Do you think it's aimed at people who are experts on the subject of yoga, or at people who know nothing about it? Explain your answer.

> Yoga is a great form of exercise that has benefits for both your body and mind. It involves lots of stretching and balancing which will make you more flexible. There are yoga classes all over the country for everyone from beginners to experts. When you know what you're doing, you can even do it by yourself at home.

Useful Language for Non-Fiction Texts

Q1   Match each sentence with the technique it uses

Sentence

a)   The latest film from director Stuart Carlisle is dull, pointless and far too long.

b)   As I stood there, tarmac setting round my ankles, I concluded that this had definitely been the right career choice for me.

c)   What right does Mr Hughes have to tell us how to live our lives? How can he pass judgement on others when he's not so perfect himself?

d)   The play was so boring I just wanted to die.

Technique

i)   irony   iii) magic threes

ii)   hyperbole   iv) rhetorical questions

Q2   Write an article about a football game using irony, magic threes, rhetorical questions and hyperbole.

Q3   Read this passage and identify an example of hyperbole, a rhetorical question, an example of irony and a magic three.

Our trip to New York was fascinating, exhilarating and exhausting. We took in the charms of Central Park, the shops of Fifth Avenue and the views from the top of the Empire State Building. What trip to the Big Apple would be complete without a Broadway show? We went to see 'The Phantom of the Opera', which is the most amazing show ever written. The only slight let down was the weather — while shivering on the top of an open-topped bus is undoubtedly fun, it would perhaps have been more enjoyable if we could have felt our fingers and toes.

Planning your Writing

Q1 You have been invited to be this week's guest writer for the newspaper column shown below. The column always has the same title, but you can interpret the title any way you want.

The Northwest Reporter

I Just Can't Stand...
The only column with a different guest writer every week

Blah blahblah blah blah blah blah blah blah blah blah Blah blahblah blah blah blah blah blah blah blah blah Blah blahblah blah blah blah blah blah blah blah blah Blah blahblah blah blah blah blah blah blah blah blah Blah blahblah blah blah blah blah blah blah blah blah Blah blahblah blah blah blah blah blah blah blah blah Blah blahblah blah blah blah blah blah blah blah blah Blah blahblah blah blah blah blah blah blah blah blah Blah blahblah blah blah blah blah blah blah blah blah blah blah blah

Blah blahblah blah blah blah blah blah blah blah blah Blah blahblah blah blah blah blah blah blah blah blah Blah blahblah blah blah blah blah blah blah blah blah Blah blahblah blah blah blah blah blah blah blah blah Blah blahblah blah blah blah blah blah blah blah blah Blah blahblah blah blah blah blah blah blah blah blah blah blah blah Blah blahblah blah blah

blah blah blah blah blah blah Blah blahblah blah blah blah blah blah blah blah blah Blah blahblah blah blah blah blah blah blah blah blah Blah blahblah blah blah blah blah blah blah blah blah Blah blahblah blah blah blah blah blah blah blah blah Blah blahblah blah blah blah blah blah blah blah blah Blah blahblah blah blah blah blah blah blah blah blah Blah blahblah blah blah blah blah blah blah blah blah Blah blahblah blah blah

Fred Bloggs

a) What kind of style do you think you need to write in for the column?

b) Jot down the key points you want to include in the column.

c) Write a detailed plan showing the structure of your column and the order of your key points.

d) Using your plan, write the newspaper column.

The one thing Humphry really couldn't stand was pedestrians sauntering out into the road in front of him.

Q2 You are going to write a speech for a podcast about a book you have read or a concert you have been to recently.

a) Jot down the key points you want to include in your speech (don't worry about putting them in order).

b) Now put your key points in order and write a detailed plan.

c) Using your plan, write the speech.

Moving Images

Q1   Write the beginning of a voice-over for a documentary about your town. The documentary will include the following things:

- The location and size of the town
- The type of industry and/or shops the town has
- Whether any famous people were born or live there

Q2   Read the short-story extract below and explain what features make it suitable for making into a film.

> The early morning sun sent rays of honey-kissed light over the park. Some tendrils of mist still lingered as Elena made her way to the river, making her shiver and wrap her arms around herself. The mist clung to her long auburn hair and left its droplets on her summery cardigan. It was only just after dawn, and the park was deserted. She couldn't help but make comparisons with a similar spring morning only a year ago. A morning that she would never forget...

Q3   The biscuits below are just about to be launched. Write a script for an advert for the biscuits.

Q4   Write a review of a film you have seen recently.
The review is for your school magazine.

Q5   Write a short story that could be the basis for a crime drama. Include lots of visual details to give the director ideas about how you imagine the characters and settings.

Re-creations

Q1 Write the introduction to a broadsheet newspaper article based on the events in a poem you have studied. Don't forget to write an appropriate headline too.

Q2 The following example is a newspaper article based on William Golding's *Lord of the Flies*. Use the example to write the beginning of a short story about the events in the article.

FEARS GROW FOR MISSING SCHOOLBOYS

A group of schoolboys is missing and feared dead after the plane carrying them was shot down somewhere over the Pacific. The wreckage of the plane was discovered 1,000 miles off the coast of Chile, with the body of the pilot, named today as Captain Frederick Armitage, still inside. The plane had been attacked by enemy forces. However, the passenger tube was missing from the plane, suggesting that the boys on board may have escaped alive. Rescue teams are searching the nearby area for signs of life.

The plane was carrying over 50 British schoolboys being evacuated from the war, including the choir of Christchurch School, London. Mrs Merridew, mother of missing choirboy Jack, spoke exclusively to our reporter this morning: "I'm so worried about my boy Jack, I just want him home again. But he can take care of himself, he's the head boy and chapter chorister. He can sing C sharp."

Q3 Choose an event from a text you have studied and use it to write an article for a women's magazine.

Q4 Write a short story based on a play you have studied. You can use lines from the play as dialogue if you want.

Q5 Choose an event from a Shakespeare play, and write a diary entry about it from the point of view of one of the main characters.

Commissions

Q1 You have been asked to do a piece of creative writing based on the theme 'Colour'.

    a) Draw a spider diagram showing your ideas.

    b) Now choose one of your ideas and use it to write a creative piece.

Q2 The following lines could be used to start the introduction of a story.

"I never want to see you again," he said.

The crash shook the room and then everything went silent.

"I can't believe we've run out of milk again."

Nothing good ever happens on a Monday.

    a) Write the introduction to a short story using one of these lines.

    b) Now write the rest of the story.

Q3 Write a column for a magazine with the heading: "If only I'd..."

Q4 Write the text for a leaflet about recycling in your area.

Descriptive Writing

Q1 Read the extract below. Underline the parts of the extract where the author has described the sight, sound and smell of the woods.

> *The night was dark with fear, but as I entered the woods it became darker. I felt so alone as the trees stared down at me from their heights. The nettles nipped angrily at my fingertips forcing me to hide my hands deep in my pockets. The sudden cry of a bat made me stop and I tried to focus my eyes on the flitting spectres as they dashed around my head. I shuffled on, inhaling the musty damp odour of the rotting leaves beneath my feet. I glanced behind me, but the edge of the wood was out of view. The only thing I could do was carry on, deeper into the biting coldness that smothered me and blurred my vision with tears.*

Q2 You have been asked to write a description of a scene in a café.
Write down a sentence for each of the following senses that help to describe the scene.

Sight   **Smell**

Touch

Sound   **Taste**

Q3 Write the introduction to a description of a scene at a Christmas fair.

Q4 Write a description of a beach in August — then describe the same beach in November.

Q5 Choose either the scene from Q2 or the scene from Q3 and write the rest of the descriptive piece.

__Narrative Writing__

Q1 Say which of the statements below are true and which are false.

    a) It can be a good idea to base a short story on something that's happened to you.

    b) Nothing that happens in real life is interesting enough to write a story about.

    c) It's often helpful to write about something you're interested in.

Q2 You have been asked to write a piece of narrative text with the title 'Space'.
Draw a spider diagram showing your ideas.

Q3 You are going to write a piece of narrative text about someone taking part in a competition.
Make notes about what will happen in each of the following stages:

        • **Beginning**

        • **Build-up**

        • **Climax**

        • **Ending**

So describe to me again the stages of a narrative text...

Q4 Choose one of your ideas from Q2 and use it to write a narrative piece with the title 'Space'.

Q5 Write a piece of narrative text with one of the following titles:

> **The Day I Will Never Forget**
>
>   **Surprise**
>
>   **Dreams**

Style and Finishing your Narrative

Q1   Read the following extract about a rabbit being chased by dogs.

> The rabbit darted through the thicket because the hunting dogs were chasing after it. There was a pack of them and their slavering tongues were lolling grotesquely. Their bloodthirsty yelps were alerting the hunters and it wasn't clear whether the dogs would manage to keep up or if they would lose the scent or if they would fall behind.

Rewrite the passage using short, punchy sentences to increase its pace.

Q2   Read the following extract about a singer.

> The audience was silent and I felt the glare of the lights on me. I hoped my nervousness did not show. I felt the band shift impatiently behind me. I took my time walking to the microphone. Still the audience was silent as they waited. I cleared my throat quietly, but then again more loudly. Another deep breath and I began. My song floated from my lungs, exactly as I wanted it to.

a)   Rewrite the passage from the perspective of the audience.

b)   Rewrite the passage from the perspective of the band.

c)   Write about how the singer feels about the experience 30 years later.

Q3   Write about a scene where two people meet in the street unexpectedly. Include both people's perspective in your writing.

Q4   Write the final paragraph of a story about a science experiment gone wrong. Don't forget to make the last line interesting.

Let me tell you a story...

You got your creative writing sorted. You became the new Stephanie Meyer. You wrote your first blockbuster aged sixteen, retired, and never did a GCSE in your life... Ah, if only it wasn't just fiction.

Answering Literature Questions

Q1   Read the question below then look at the points in the box. Decide which of the points would **not** be good points to include in the answer, and write them down.

> *What do we learn about equality in Animal Farm, and how does Orwell achieve this?*

<u>Points for my answer:</u>

* Examples of inequality amongst the animals.

* How Orwell shows the difference between the way the animals treat each other when they have no power and when some of them do.

* The way George Orwell was brought up.

* Examples of apparent harmony amongst the animals.

* Different types of farming methods.

* The ideas about equality we are left with at the end of the book.

* One of the main characters.

Q2   Write down what type of question you think each of the below are — whether they're asking about:
• **theme**   • **setting**   • **characterisation**   • **writer's skills**

a)   What is the significance of the island in **Lord of the Flies**?

b)   How does Shakespeare present the character of Feste in this extract?

c)   What ideas about class does Jane Austen present in **Pride and Prejudice**?

d)   Compare the language used by the poets in **Charge of the Light Brigade** and one other poem.

Q3   Pick a character from one of the texts you've read in class. Explain how you feel about that character and how you think the author has made you feel that way. Remember to use evidence from the text to back up your argument.

Writing About Characters

Q1 Read the paragraphs below about characters, and write down which character assessment suits them best.

a) *Jane ran into the school yard with a sudden burst of energy like a gust of wind. Her excited laughter could be heard from the car park as she quickly flung her bag to the floor, grabbed her friend Sophie and twirled them both around and around in a dizzying spin.*

Jane is:

i)   A lazy, unfriendly and boring girl who doesn't like playing outdoors.

ii) A young, excitable school girl with lots of energy, who likes to have fun with friends.

iii) A tired, sad old lady who can't walk very far.

b) *Mrs. Wilkes saw from the corner of the door that Mr. Wilkes was sleeping. His fluffy, white hair seemed to cradle his chubby, smiling face like a bonnet, as he slowly inhaled and exhaled the late afternoon air. She chuckled to herself quietly, before closing the door and heading back out into the garden.*

Mr. Wilkes is:

i)   A restless, fierce man who everyone is afraid of, including his wife.

ii) A highly strung, arrogant male model with chiselled cheek bones and an athletic physique.

iii) A peaceful, elderly, but child-like man, whose wife probably mothers him.

Q2 Write out the speech below and underline the parts which you think show what type of character Puck is. Then write at least two sentences describing what you think Puck is like.

> PUCK: Captain of our fairy band,
> Helena is here at hand,
> And the youth, mistook by me,
> Pleading for a lover's fee,
> Shall we their fond pageant see?
> Lord, what fools these mortals be!
>
> OBERON: Stand aside: the noise they make
> Will cause Demitrius to awake.
>
> PUCK: Then will two at once woo one;
> That must needs be sport alone;
> And those things do best please me
> That befall prepost'rously.
>
> Act III, Scene II, *A Midsummer Night's Dream*

Q3 Read the paragraph below and identify one detail about a) the character's appearance, b) his actions and c) his language that reveal something about him.

> Carlos's thin, spindly fingers tapped out a restless rhythm on the tabletop, adding to the air of unease. His narrow eyes scanned the room, and his displeasure at everything he saw was clear on his scowling face.
> "What a disgusting place," he declared. "It's positively barbaric."

Writing About Characters

Q1   For each paragraph below, write a short sentence describing what the main characters' appearance, actions and language are like.

a)   The Wicked Queen of Avalonia knew that she was doomed to a fate of certain execution within the coming days, for a crime she did not commit. She had nothing left to lose, and was now free to seek revenge for the many years of ill treatment she had suffered at the hands of her cruel chiropodist. However, she thought it best to keep quiet about it all, not wanting to upset everyone.

b)   Mr Finchley just hadn't been the same after winning the lottery three years ago. His neighbours soon noticed that he'd stopped going to the local pub on a Friday night, and, apart from the six-foot-high electric fencing around his house, everybody seemed to wonder what he spent all his money on. People began to call him greedy and snobby. Then one day in June, the word got around that he had died suddenly, leaving all of his fortune to John the milkman.

c)   Lovely Mrs Tabble was a kind old dinner lady, who took good care of the children at Saint Judith's, and always brought special sweets for them on Fridays. Katie, a girl from school, was very surprised and saddened to see Mrs Tabble angrily kicking her dog in the park, one afternoon in the summer holidays.

Q2   Quoting from the paragraphs in Q1, write a few short sentences to answer the questions below:

a)   *How can we tell that the Wicked Queen of Avalonia isn't really wicked?*

b)   *How do Mr Finchley's actions make us distrust the neighbours' opinion of him?*

c)   *How does Katie's reaction to Mrs Tabble affect our view of her?*

Q3   Briefly rewrite the three stories outlined in Q1 from the point of view of each of the main characters.

Q4   Read the passage below and use it to work out how Louisa feels about Maddy.

Louisa stared at Maddy in disbelief. She couldn't imagine why her friend — her best friend — was treating her this way. They'd known each other since primary school, and were as close as sisters. Maddy's betrayal was made even worse by the fact that she had been in a similar situation just a few months before, and Louisa had stood by her, supported her and defended her to anyone who had dared criticise her.

Section Five — Writing About Prose, Drama and Poetry

The Writer's Ideas, Attitudes and Feelings

Q1   Choosing from the questions below, write down the ones which you think are **message questions**.

    a)   *How do we get to know the character of Puck in* **A Midsummer Night's Dream**?

    b)   *What do you think Shakespeare is saying about love in* **Romeo and Juliet**?

    c)   *What methods does Larkin employ to describe the world of work in* **Toads Revisited**?

    d)   *What does* **Educating Rita** *tell us about the way society operates?*

Q2   Write out the points below, dividing them into four lists, headed: **Theme**, **Characters**, **Tone** and **Title**.

> * *Lee uses the other characters to show the different aspects of society in 1930s America.*
>
> * *'To Kill a Mockingbird' gets its title because of a comment in the novel — "it's said to be a sin to kill a mockingbird because they do no harm to anyone, all they do is sing and make beautiful music." The title suggests Lee's view on the attitudes and events of the novel.*
>
> * *Sadness and anger about the loss of innocence in the novel and the sinful way that good people can be treated.*
>
> * *The novel is about a series of events in the childhoods of Jem and Scout Finch. Tom Robinson is accused of rape by a white woman and is automatically assumed to be guilty because he is black. Atticus Finch defends him in court even though he knows that the jury will almost certainly find him guilty.*
>
> * *Main characters are Atticus Finch, a lawyer who represents a black man accused of rape, and his young children Scout and Jem, who view the events of the novel through innocent eyes.*
>
> * *Lee is generally sympathetic towards black people and the way they are unfairly treated by white people in the Maycomb community.*
>
> * *Attitudes to race in the black and white communities are explored throughout Harper Lee's narrative.*

Q3   Using the brief overview you created in Q2 as a guide, write down which of these sentences you think best describes the writer's message in **To Kill a Mockingbird**.

    a)   Shooting birds is acceptable, as long as they are not mockingbirds.

    b)   Good, honest people can be treated badly by others due to intolerance and prejudice.

    c)   1930s America was a difficult place for children to grow up.

    d)   American society in the 1930s was racist and prejudiced, which could lead to terrible injustices for innocent people.

Q4   Answer these questions about **Goldilocks and the Three Bears**.

    a)   Using the story **Goldilocks and the Three Bears** as your text, create a brief overview like the one in Q2, with the headings: Story, Characters, Tone and Title.

    b)   Using your overview, write a brief sentence describing what you think the writer's message is in **Goldilocks and the Three Bears**.

Different Cultures

Q1   Write out the words below. Circle those which are unfamiliar to you and underline the words which are spelt so they sound like an accent or dialect.

shrine	cumdach	everyting	everything
important	bigibigi	laidak	rogue
chifforobe	cabinet	this morning	dis marnin'

Q2   Write down everything from this extract that tells you it is from a different culture.

> This is how I make a living.
>
> During the week I work at the Institute teaching English to people who want to live elsewhere. I wish I could join them but instead I'm trapped here by my own heritage. At the weekend I buy and sell cars to subsidise my pitiful wage, which is barely enough to survive on.
>
> Viktor can see the harbour from his building, so he comes over and tells me when there's a Japanese ship in port. I go down to the harbour and talk to the sailors, then we go and sit in a cafe and have a drink. I like talking to them; they tell wonderful tales of their homeland which I'd love to visit. Usually it turns out they have a car to sell because they know they can get a good price here. So I take the car off their hands.
>
> The Japanese cars are right-hand drive, but that doesn't bother my customers. Most of them are stupid country muzhiks who don't know what side of the road they should be driving anyway. In a way I envy them — they have no idea that they could have a better life.
>
> When I've paid the sailor and given Viktor his bottle of vodka and paid off the harbour master and paid my dues to the mafia, I can finally take the car out to the villages.
>
> In summer it's hell because the roads are so dusty; in winter it's hell because of the snow and ice; and in spring and autumn the roads are a sea of mud. Maybe winter's the best because at least the cars don't get so dirty.

[What a bargain.]

Q3   Write two or three paragraphs about the extract in Q2 to answer the question below. Don't forget to use quotes to back up what you say.

> *How does the writer show the narrator's feelings about his way of life?*

The Writer's Techniques

Q1 Rewrite the paragraph below in the style of:

a) a spooky murder mystery
b) a romantic love story
c) a news report

> Julia sat by the fire and kept warm. She knew that Martin, the boy from the village, had said he would be there at eight o'clock to take her out. It was now eight thirty, and Julia looked over to the window to see if she could spot his car, but it was raining, and there was no sign of him.

Q2 Answer these questions about Ms. Simmonds.

a) Using the information below, write down which type of character you think Ms. Simmonds is.

> Ms. Simmonds: *"I am very pleased you are able to come to my party. It will start promptly at seven thirty. Please dress according to the standards I have indicated on the invitation. One bottle of medium-priced wine will suffice as a gift."*

  i)   A very organised woman, who knows what she wants.
  ii)   A bumbling idiot, who can't string two sentences together.
  iii) A very funny woman, who has everybody in stitches.

b) Choosing from the list below, write down the styles used to create the character of Ms. Simmonds.

  i)   Short, simple sentences.
  ii)   Lots of fancy comparisons.
  iii) Unusual, difficult words.
  iv)   Formal wording.
  v)   No fancy comparisons.

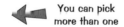 **You can pick more than one**

Q3 Answer these questions about the paragraph below.

a) Copy out the paragraph below, and underline the bits that you feel help to set the scene.

> Julia sat in the lonely old vicarage, huddling in close to the fire, trying to keep warm. The huge stone walls were damp and gave off a mouldy stench. Almost too cold to move, she forced herself to turn and face the cobweb covered windows, which looked out onto the darkness of the windswept causeway.

b) Now write a couple of sentences to say how this is supposed to make us feel.

Q4 Write a brief paragraph which **foreshadows** the disappearance of Martin in Q1.

Reading Plays

Q1   Read the plot outlines, then write down which of these Shakespeare
     plays is a **tragedy**, which one's a **comedy**, and which one's a **history**.

   Twelfth Night — A young woman called Viola dresses up as a man. A woman called Olivia
        falls in love with Viola in her new outfit and Viola falls in love with her boss, Orsino...
        meanwhile the other characters are always drunk or fighting... they all live happily ever after.

   King Henry V — based on the story of the real Henry V. Henry goes to France with an English army where
        he fights a battle at Agincourt, and wins a massive victory.

   King Lear — Lear, a mythical king, hands England over to his two selfish and power-hungry daughters. He ends up
        mad and homeless, and dies heartbroken when his mistakes cost his one honest and loving daughter her life.

Q2   Read the passages below from *Much Ado About Nothing*, and write down which is:
     a) a **monologue**,   b) a **dialogue**,   c) an **aside**,   d) a **soliloquy**.

i)
> WATCH: *(aside)* I know that Deformed; a' has
> been a vile thief this seven years; a' goes up and
> down like a gentleman: I remember his name.

   Act III, Scene III

HINT: The Friar's explaining a plan,
so he's probably <u>talking to someone</u>.

ii)
> FRIAR: Marry, this well carried, shall on her behalf
>   Change slander to remorse; that is some good:
>   But not for that dream I on this strange course,
>   But on this travail look for greater birth.
>   She dying, as it must be so maintain'd,
>   Upon the instant that she was accus'd,
>   Shall be lamented, pitied and excus'd
>   Of every hearer; for it so falls out
>   That what we have we prize not to the worth
>   Whiles we enjoy it.....

   Act IV, Scene I

iii)
> BENEDICK: I do much wonder that one
> man, seeing how much another man is a
> fool when he dedicates his behaviours to
> love, will, after he hath laughed at such
> shallow follies in others, become the
> argument of his own scorn by falling in love:
> and such a man is Claudio... He was wont
> to speak plain and to the purpose, like an
> honest man and a soldier; and now he is
> turned orthographer; his words are a very
> fantastical banquet, just so many strange
> dishes. May I be so converted, and see with
> these eyes?

   Act II, Scene III

HINT: Benedick's talking about
fairly personal stuff, so he's
probably <u>talking to himself</u>.

iv)
BENEDICK:	Lady Beatrice, have you wept all this while?
BEATRICE:	Yea, and I will weep a while longer.
BENEDICK:	I will not desire that.
BEATRICE:	You have no reason; I do it freely.

   Act IV, Scene I

Q3   Write out the passage from Q2 iv), and include brief details of the stage design, any action that takes
     place, and put in brackets how the characters are speaking. Aim to create a very sad, depressing scene.

Writing About Poetry

Q1 Write out the sentences below and underline the words that you think are used for either their **assonance**, **alliteration** or **onomatopoeia**. Write down assonance, alliteration or onomatopoeia after each sentence.

a) Cute Carly loved the cuddly clown she got for Christmas.

b) Sheila leaped across the heath to where the sheep were fast asleep.

c) The snake hissed at the guide as he tried to hush the noisy children behind him.

d) Rachel ran across the reading room with a thud, as the buzzing bees chased her.

Q2 Poets include pauses, or break up the lines of poetry in a particular way to add style, and to draw emphasis to certain words. Write down each name for the types of methods being used in the examples below.

a) And wrinkled lip and sneer of cold command
Tell that its sculptor well those passions read

b) 'Out 'mong the sheep, her be,' they said,
Should properly have been abed;

c) And yonder all before us lie
Deserts of vast eternity.

Q3 Write down whether the lines below are in a regular rhythm or irregular rhythm.

a) *The baker knew the flour had not been bought.*

b) *But baking bread was something he did exceptionally well.*

Q4 Poets can change the pace of a poem by using words that make it sound either quick, slow, clunky or graceful. Add or remove words from the clunky line below, to make it sound: a) **quick**; b) **slow**; c) **graceful**.

> Glenda knew it was time to go when the traffic light went green and the cars behind her followed.

Q5 The tone of a poem is created when words are chosen to evoke certain feelings, such as anger, happiness, or regret. Rewrite the line in Q3 a), and add words which create a tone of: a) **anger**; b) **happiness**; c) **fear**.

Useful Literature Words

Q1 Write out the sentences below and place them under their correct heading of **simile** or **metaphor**.

> * My boss is an immature little baby.
>
> * Mark's father was as nice as pie when he came home.
>
> * The sea was like a pane of glass.
>
> * The people of the world are tenants and God is the landlord.
>
> * The plane soared as effortlessly as a bird into the blue sky.
>
> * Jason's new bike was the Rolls Royce of mountain bikes.
>
> * The Moon is the mother of the planets.
>
> * The woman in the pub was howling like a banshee.

Q2 Choosing from the list below, write down which idea or emotion you think the imagery of the horses symbolises in this sentence:

> **Sarah leaned on her crutches as she watched the horses bolt away from the starting line with ease and vigour.**

i)   You shouldn't break your leg if you like watching horses.

ii) Sarah's love of horses.

iii) Sarah's desire to be able to walk again.

Q3 Write a few sentences explaining why John's liking for the food in the sentence below is **ambiguous**.

> **John couldn't eat another thing at Madge's dinner party. He was very interested to know what ingredients she had been using.**

Q4 Write out the sentences below and underline the **ironic** bits.

> Christopher had always been a brainy grade-A student. So everybody had really expected him to fail disastrously at the children's spelling competition.
>
> Sally was her usual inconspicuous self, with a bright pink and purple T-shirt and yellow striped jeans.

Q5 Read the sentences below and underline examples of **emotive language**.

> Jessica looked over the devastation and tried to hold back tears. What had once been a beautiful garden had been butchered and ruined. Where there had once been acres of lush, green lawns there was now a covering of cruel concrete. The pond, with its laughing, dancing fountain, was no more, and her lovingly-tended roses had been viciously ripped out. The heart of the garden was gone, replaced by cold, unfeeling stone.

Comparing

Q1 The two poems below share the same main subject matter. Read them both through and then choose from the list below, what you think the main subject of each poem is:
a) **Hearts**, b) **Talking**, c) **Love**, or d) **Marriage**.

To His Coy Mistress

Had we but world enough, and time,
This coyness, Lady, were no crime,
We would sit down and think which way
To walk and pass our long love's day.
Thou by the Indian Ganges' side
Shouldst rubies find; I by the tide
Of Humber would complain. I would
Love you ten years before the Flood,
And you should, if you please, refuse
Till the conversion of the Jews.
My vegetable love should grow
Vaster than empires, and more slow;
An hundred years should go to praise
Thine eyes, and on thy forehead gaze;
Two hundred to adore each breast;
But thirty thousand to the rest;
An age at least to every part,
And the last age should show your heart.
For, Lady, you deserve this state,
Nor would I love at lower rate.

But at my back I always hear
Time's wingèd chariot hurrying near;
And yonder all before us lie
Deserts of vast eternity.
Thy beauty shall no more be found,
Nor, in thy marble vault, shall sound
My echoing song; then worms shall try
That long preserved virginity,
And your quaint honour turn to dust,
And into ashes all my lust.
The grave's a fine and private place,
But none, I think, do there embrace.

Now therefore, while the youthful hue
Sits on thy skin like morning dew,
And while thy willing soul transpires
At every pore with instant fires,
Now let us sport us while we may,
And now, like amorous birds of prey,
Rather at once our time devour
Than languish in his slow-chapt power.
Let us roll all our strength and all
Our sweetness up into one ball,
And tear our pleasures with rough strife
Through the iron gates of life.
Thus, though we cannot make our sun
Stand still, yet we will make him run.

Andrew Marvell

Sonnet 116

Let me not to the marriage of true minds
Admit impediments; love is not love
Which alters when it alteration finds,
Or bends with the remover to remove.
O no it is an ever-fixéd mark
That looks on tempests and is never shaken;
It is the star to every wand'ring bark,
Whose worth's unknown, although his height be taken.
Love's not Time's fool, though rosy lips and cheeks
Within his bending sickle's compass come;
Love alters not with his brief hours and weeks,
But bears it out even to the edge of doom.
    If this be error and upon me proved,
    I never writ, nor no man ever loved.

William Shakespeare

Comparing

Q1   Using the poems on page 37, choose which paragraph below best compares the main idea in each.

    a)   Both poems talk about love and time, but they have contrasting ideas about how long love lasts. Shakespeare talks about the "brief hours and weeks" of love; whereas Marvell writes about spending "an hundred years" just admiring his mistress.

    b)   Both poems are about love and death. Shakespeare talks about "doom"; his poem is a bit depressing. Marvell writes that love is pointless after death, and talks about "dust", "ashes" and the "grave" which is quite morbid.

    c)   Both poems are about love, but they have different attitudes to it. In the first poem, Shakespeare describes love as constant and timeless — writing that "Love alters not" with time. In contrast, Marvell's poem is much more urgent as its narrator tries to encourage the subject of the poem to surrender her "long preserved virginity" to him.

Q2   Explain what effects you think the following aspects of style and structure have in the poems.

    a) Irony and exaggeration in 'To His Coy Mistress'

    b) Regular rhyme scheme in both poems

    c) Sonnet form in 'Sonnet 116'

    d) Rhyming couplets in 'To His Coy Mistress'

Q3   Using your answers from Q2, write a paragraph to compare the style and structure of each poem, and explain how this relates to the ideas of the love in each.

Q4   Write a few paragraphs comparing and contrasting the language used in each poem. Don't forget to say how the language relates to the main idea outlined in Q1, and give examples.

Q5   Using the information you've got already from the questions above, and your own examples from the texts, write about a page to answer the following question:

> *What methods do Shakespeare and Marvell use in order to describe and convey their ideas about love?*

Compering is more fun — you get to make fentestic jokes...
Brrrr...is there a chilly draught in here, or is the evil spirit of Comparing Questions passing through?...

Standard English

Q1   Copy out the following sentences under the headings "Standard English" or "Non-Standard English".

a)   When I saw him, I was like, oh my God!

b)   Dinnae fash yersel' hen.

c)   This track was number one for six weeks in 1998.

d)   Whatever happens, I will keep my promise to you.

e)   Lenneisha and Zaria and me were chuffed to be asked to the party.

f)   I love the colour of that dress on you.

Q2   Copy out these sentences and underline the words and/or phrases that are not Standard English.

a)   If I had known that yesterday, I'd've never done it, you know?

b)   I was watching Big Brother, right, last night, right.

c)   I can't believe we lost — I was gutted!

d)   Fifteen minutes into the film, Nari chucked up everywhere.

e)   That'll be done in a jiffy, sweet as a nut.

f)   Jason — laters!

Q3   Rewrite these sentences using 'them' or 'those', and 'who' or 'which' in correct Standard English.

a)   You know them pens of yours? Let me see them.

b)   That is the man which sold the most records in 1960.

c)   Do you still get them headaches?

d)   Those? They're horrible! Try them other shoes on instead.

e)   It was the poster of Will Smith who fell off the wall.

f)   It was *my* sister which won the high jump on Sports Day.

Q4   Read the following examples carefully, then rewrite them using Standard English.

a)   Charlie went mad when he heard all them rumours about Tilly.

b)   Some random guy came up and asked me to snap him with my camera.

c)   Measure 4 Measure by Shakespeare does stuff about justice in it.

d)   It's not like watching the TV, it's, like, much better.

e)   I'm always telling you to be on time, innit?

Punctuation

Q1   Rewrite these sentences with capital letters and full stops in the right places.

   a)   the bicycle swerved to avoid the woman it was too late they collided

   b)   margaret has lived by the sea all her life it was a shock when she moved to the city

   c)   the park stretched away from the house its rolling fields were pleasant to the eye

   d)   i have change for the meter you can take these fifty pence pieces

   e)   my feet are aching let's stop and have a cup of tea

   f)   don't worry if you see a lion they have already eaten today

   g)   everyone likes football i want mexico to beat france

> Hint: If you're not sure, say the sentence out loud. Listen carefully for the <u>pause</u> marking the end of a group of words.

Q2   Some of these sentences use commas correctly and some do not.
Rewrite the ones that are wrong, correcting the mistakes.

   a)   Despite many appeals, including a high profile campaign over Christmas, drinking and driving figures have not substantially improved.

   b)   Turn left at the traffic lights then right then right again and it's just on the left.

   c)   I was late as, you might well imagine.

   d)   Books papers photos clothes and ornaments were thrown all over the floor.

   e)   Crithers McFosfate legendary horror writer died yesterday in his California home.

   f)   The horse hearing a loud noise took fright and bolted.

   g)   Yesterday was all right, I suppose, but today is going to be even better.

Q3   Each of these examples needs a semi-colon or a colon to make them into proper sentences.
Copy them out with the correct punctuation.

   a)   You found an old friend__I found a new one.

   b)   He had a face you'd never forget__it was hideous.

   c)   It's raining__my hair will be ruined.

   d)   There's only one solution__you'll have to go there yourself.

   e)   This kit contains__twelve plastic pieces, a tube of adhesive, three colours of paint, two brushes of differing sizes and a set of instructions for assembly.

   f)   I'm a big fan of orange__my sister loves purple.

Apostrophes

Q1 Change these phrases by writing them out again *without* the apostrophe.

> e.g. the cat's bowl = the bowl belonging to the cat

a) Mum's briefcase

b) her pupil's progress

c) Arsenal's chances

d) the skeleton's bones

e) Terry's satsuma

f) Hannah's calculator

Q2 Write two headings: 'Singular' and 'Plural'. Copy the underlined words under the appropriate columns.

a) the <u>children's</u> party

b) <u>Henry Kissinger's</u> wife

c) the <u>mice's</u> droppings

d) the <u>flowers'</u> petals

e) the <u>soldiers'</u> guns

f) my <u>mother's friends'</u> laughter

g) <u>Colonel Hitchpankster's</u> men

h) the <u>cows'</u> milk

Q3 Rewrite each sentence making corrections to its/it's where needed.

a) Goodness! Its three-thirty.

b) The car had a dent in its wing.

c) Its cold enough to be October.

d) Who knows what its called?

e) It's often confused for a parrot.

f) The factory belched smoke from it's chimney.

Q4 Rewrite the underlined words in full. Then underline the letters the apostrophe replaced.

a) I <u>didn't</u> phone you last night because I was painting my goldfish.

b) You <u>shouldn't</u> let him cut your hair.

c) We <u>can't</u> leave now — <u>they'd</u> think we were rude.

d) <u>I'll</u> go in first. You wait here.

e) <u>You're</u> the last person <u>I'd</u> want to be stuck in a lift with!

f) You can tell them why <u>we're</u> so late.

Q5 Now make as big a list as you can of words where an apostrophe is used for omission. Use the words from Q4 to start you off.

Q6 Copy out the following sentences under two headings: 'Possession' and 'Omission'.

a) The donkey's straw hat blew away.

b) It wasn't me!

c) They are dad's boots.

d) He's fifteen, isn't he?

e) They'll win nothing this year.

f) The boys' room was tidy.

Speech Marks

Q1　Rewrite these sentences using speech marks.　The first one's been done for you.
Try to use some more descriptive verbs instead of plain old 'said' while you're at it.

a)　DAVID:　　It's the third time I have come last in the 100m this year.
e.g. "It's the third time I have come last in the 100m this year," sighed David.

b)　CRAIG:　　I love mashed up bananas! They're great!

c)　JUDY:　　Do I look stupid to you?

d)　FRED:　　You have had your last chance, pal. It's payback time.

e)　KEELEY:　　Look after yourself. It's not *my* job, is it?

Q2　Rewrite these examples with capital letters in the correct places.

a)　Alex tore out of the room and shouted, "get down! It's about to blow!"

b)　"hold it right there, buster," yelled the cop.

c)　Kate shrieked, "that's the worst photo of me I've *ever* seen!"

d)　"hold the line, please," said Jade, "i need to write that down."

Q3　Rewrite these examples with either a comma, a question mark or a full stop in the blanks.

a)　"What do you think you're doing __" he shouted.

b)　She turned to him with tears in her eyes and said__ "You know I can't."

c)　She smiled and said, "This is the best pizza ever__"

d)　The fireman asked, "Are there any more people in there__"

e)　Mr. Brown turned to the hotel rep and cried__ "This is the worst holiday I have ever had__"

Q4　Write the following sentences out with all the punctuation correctly in place.

a)　you don't need to do that yourself said Emma

b)　scale the wall scale *that* castle wall scoffed the soldier you must be joking sir

c)　the judge cleared his throat and announced you have been found guilty of the murder of your wife

d)　the buried treasure is mine when we find it snapped the captain understand

e)　is it all right if he comes to school asked Mary pointing at her little lamb

f)　the wettest weather will be in the west smiled the weather girl

g)　select only the freshest ingredients for your larder simpered the TV chef

h)　if I pick the winner tonight I'll share my winnings with you said Dad

i)　fifteen hundred fans gathered in the centre of town to welcome the cup-winning team home announced the news presenter

j)　bob stuck his head out of the changing room and said can you bring me a size smaller please, dave

Negatives

Q1   Make two headings: 'Positive' and 'Negative' and copy out the sentences under the correct one. Look for clues in the words.

a)   United will never win in Europe.

b)   Barry forgot to bring his trainers for P.E.

c)   Julian swore he wasn't at the scene of the crime.

d)   Always wear a helmet on a scooter.

e)   Never wear a live monkey on a scooter.

f)   Use the juice of three apples.

Q2   Rewrite these negative sentences, changing them so that they use positive words.

a)   Never look on the dull side of life.

b)   I wouldn't start a long car journey without checking tyre pressure first.

c)   You know Delaney never tells the truth.

d)   Isn't that your house over there?

e)   There were no parking spaces in the car parks in town on Saturday.

Q3   All of these sentences use double negatives. Rewrite them so they make better sense. There may be more than one option.

a)   Nobody never went to my Alfred's grave.

b)   None of my family isn't clever.

c)   You shouldn't never stick your wet fingers in electric plug holes.

d)   None of his kids look nothing like him.

e)   Police! Don't nobody move.

f)   I wouldn't never have done it if I'd known.

Q4   The answer to all these questions is 'none'. Write out the answers in full sentences.

a)   How many holidays have you been on this year?

b)   How many biscuits did you eat yesterday?

c)   How many women perm their ears?

d)   How many traffic jams were there in town on Sunday?

e)   How many roads must a man walk down before he becomes grown up?

f)   How many teeth do you have in your head?

Q5   Correct these sentences so they are clear.

a)   I don't get no sleep at night.

b)   My baby ain't got no money.

c)   We never didn't love each other at all.

d)   Nobody misses you like I don't.

e)   I ain't sleeping none tonight.

f)   Never give me no goodbye.

Sentences

Q1   All the verbs in these sentences are incorrect. Rewrite the sentences without errors.

a)   I went back to my friend's house tomorrow, because he wasn't in today.

b)   My cousins comes to visit every summer.

c)   Every Wednesday next year, I went to Creative Sequinning classes.

d)   Here — I knows you, don't I?

e)   My brother play in a one-man band.

f)   When I was young, I am the cleverest in my class.

Q2   Rewrite these examples, improving the sentences so they flow with style.

a)   Karen walked back the long way and so did Karen's mum.

b)   Hippos who can't hold their noses under water die by drowning and hippos who
     don't eat much die by getting too thin to live.

c)   The best way to catch a butterfly is to catch a butterfly when it is resting.

d)   We don't know who it was who killed Sandra Bigginbottom but the person who
     killed her can't be very far away.

e)   It was midnight. Just after midnight there was a noise. Daveena heard it. Roxy just
     kept sleeping though.

f)   Too many cars are on the streets. There is a lot of traffic. There are lots of cars
     especially in the morning and the evening.

Q3   Rearrange the sentences in this paragraph so they're in clear chronological order.

> Brazil won. It was a brilliant final. Some people were sad that South Korea didn't make it
> to the final. I was sad that England got knocked out in the semi-final, though they just
> managed to beat Argentina in the quarter-final so there was a bit of consolation. I was
> pleased Ireland got beyond the second round too. I have to say, though, that the First Round
> is my favourite bit because there is football on telly three times a day and all the teams are
> full of hope and energy. I thought it was a terrible shame that Scotland and Wales did not
> qualify at all, but I am sure they will next time.

Q4   Now rewrite this paragraph, starting each sentence in a different way to make it more interesting.

> By the second day, Clarence noticed that the bump on his neck had
> grown swollen and red. By the third day, Clarence looked in the mirror
> and saw that the swelling had increased to the size of a golf ball. By the
> fourth day, he had to hold his head to the left because the swelling was
> so huge he couldn't hold his head straight. By the fifth day, the itching
> was unbearable and the lump was the same size as a bowling ball. By
> the last day of the week, Clarence realised that this itchy lump was
> no mere swelling. He realised it was no hideous allergic reaction to an
> insect bite. He realised that he was, in fact, growing a second head.

Writing Varied Sentences

Q1   Copy out these sentences and underline the two things being compared.

   a)   Polly's hair was more golden than the sun.

   b)   The bird's egg was smaller than a gobstopper.

   c)   The oak tree's trunk was wider than a bus.

   d)   Her voice was louder than a police car's siren.

   e)   Rosie's eyes were brighter than twinkling stars.

Q2   Explain what the nouns in each part of Q1 have in common.

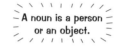

A noun is a person or an object.

Q3   Try to compare the following with things to help the reader visualise them.

   a)   a tower block

   b)   a stream

   c)   a football crowd

   d)   a smile

   e)   a hairstyle

For comparisons to really work, the two things need to have something in common.

Q4   Write two complete sentences for each pair of words, using 'as' in one and 'like' in the other.

e.g. feet, stilton → His <u>feet</u> smell <u>as</u> bad as a six-month-old <u>stilton</u>.
                → His <u>feet</u> smell <u>like</u> six-month-old <u>stilton</u>.

   a)   cold   iceberg

   b)   unfriendly   snarling dog

   c)   exciting   roller coaster

   d)   teeth   gravestones

   e)   hair   mouldy straw

   f)   quiet   mice

   g)   voice   angel

   h)   path   ribbon

Q5   Choose either type of comparison from Q4 to exaggerate these examples as much as you can.

   a)   Martha is funny.

   b)   The hill is steep.

   c)   The boy usually eats a lot.

   d)   The dog is smelly.

   e)   The old man grumbles all the time.

   f)   Briony is good at Maths.

   g)   Yasmine is always tired.

   h)   Anna never stops talking.

Writing Varied Sentences

Q1 **Liven up these descriptions by using more varied and interesting adjectives.**

a) I had a lovely birthday. I got loads of lovely cards and Mum gave me a lovely bracelet. Then, I had a lovely party and we ate a lovely cake.

b) This is absolutely the right time to move house. The market is absolutely full of people buying and selling, and it's absolutely certain you'll get a good price. A good idea? Absolutely!

c) Look at these great trainers. I got them for a great price. They look great on my feet and they are great for comfort. If you got a pair, they'd look great on you too.

Q2 **Make these paragraphs less boring by changing some of the repeated words.**

a) We went on a school trip last week. We went by coach to Dizzyland. When we got there, I went on six rides. The best I went on was called 'The Demon'. Dominic went on it four times. By the time we went home, we were calling him Demonic Dominic.

b) When I saw Rebecca I said that Amarpreet had said that she wasn't my friend. Rebecca said that she hadn't said anything like that and she didn't know why Amarpreet had said that to me. I got angry and said I didn't care what she said. Then she got upset and she said she didn't want to be my friend anyway.

c) I watched the TV last night. There was a football match on that I wanted to watch. Afterwards, I went out and watched my cat try to catch a bird. It didn't manage. It just watched it for ages.

Q3 **Broaden your vocabulary — write out the 'fancy' word next to the simple word it matches.**

a) horrible   i) nonsensical
b) easy   ii) uninteresting
c) stupid   iii) complex
d) boring   iv) unappealing
e) difficult   v) unchallenging

Q4 **Use each of the fancy words from Q3 in a sentence which shows its meaning.**

Q5 **Rewrite the following examples changing some of the simple words for fancy ones.**

a) The train left five minutes late.
b) Spain was quite a poor country until only a few years ago.
c) The magazine had loads of good stuff in it about make-up.
d) The midfield kept letting the other team through to attack.
e) You are much better at writing varied sentences now than you were at the start of this page.

I've got a broad vocabulary — it's extensive, expansive, er, wide...

Don't get bogged down using the same old words all the time. You want to make your work sound interesting and be fun to read. No really you do. It's everyone's burning desire. Surely.

Writing Varied Sentences

Q1   Make two headings: 'Literal' and 'Metaphorical' and copy these sentences under the correct one.

    a)   By the last fence the jockey was carrying his horse.

    b)   The mountain spring was clear and fresh.

    c)   The baby cried all night.

    d)   My party went with a bang.

    e)   He always shoots my ideas down in flames.

    f)   When I tell you things they go in one ear and out the other.

    g)   She was so angry, her face went red.

    h)   After her promotion, Kate was walking on air.

Q2   Write a list of as many common metaphorical expressions as you can.

Hint: sports commentators and journalists are quite fond of using them...

Q3   Sometimes words can be used to suggest an image.
Copy these sentences and underline the word(s) used in this way.

    a)   She sailed across the room.

    b)   He was so angry! At half-time he exploded at them.

    c)   Her face shone in delight.

    d)   She rattled off the points in favour of the proposal.

    e)   She sieved through the application forms quickly.

    f)   The sergeant-major towered above the new recruit.

Q4   For the examples in Q3 explain what images the words are trying to suggest.

Q5   Replace the verb "walked" in the sentence below with a more figurative word to convey the emotions a) to f). Use the words from the box.

He walked across the room.

| sloshed | slimed | pirouetted |
| crashed | limped | leapt | thundered |

    a)   angrily   d)   confidently

    b)   sneakily   e)   drunkenly

    c)   apologetically   f)   impatiently

Q6   Add to the list and see how many different ways you can make him cross the room just by choosing good figurative words.

Language Words

Q1   Copy out these sentences and underline all the nouns.

    a)   The gardener took the shears and trimmed the hedge every Tuesday throughout the summer.

    b)   Sian and Cati had been friends for six years and there was a strong sense of loyalty and trust between them.

    c)   Clearly, the directors must decide whether Paterson has enough skill to keep his place in the team.

    d)   All the things for the picnic were spread out on a tartan rug on the grass.

    e)   To build the cathedral, from the first brick to the last piece of wooden carving, took one hundred and thirty-three years.

    f)   Tragically, four field mice and a slowworm were killed when the river burst its banks.

Q2   Now use a different colour, or shape of line, and underline the verbs in the sentences in Q1.

Q3   Replace the adjectives in the sentences below with more interesting ones from the box to liven them up.

absorbing	colossal	bewildering	excruciating
minute	ostentatious	odious	attractive

    a)   There was a small rip in his trousers.

    b)   Look at that disgusting dog.

    c)   I read this book in four days it was so interesting.

    d)   The maths test was too hard.

    e)   She dyed her hair bright pink just to be eye-catching.

    f)   They ran up a huge bill at the bar.

    g)   She bought a really nice jumper in that shop.

    h)   When I broke my finger the pain was really bad.

"My name's not Bill."

Q4   Make these sentences more visually descriptive by inserting an adverb of your choice.

    a)   Rory walked into the room.

    b)   Felicity opened her mouth and shrieked.

    c)   Arabella curtseyed.

    d)   Bruce pointed at the crowd.

    e)   Quentin lay back in the hammock and sighed.

    f)   "How could you?" said Dilys.

    g)   "Why is it always me that has to wash the dishes?" asked Matt.

    h)   Chris was unaware that the bull was running at him and Owen.

Checking Practice

Q1   Rewrite this review from an Australian film magazine into Standard English.
You can change as many words as you want but must keep the same meaning.

> "Access Denied" is the fourth film by megastar Jean-Pierre Den Bosch to hit the screens in the new millennium. His fans won't be disappointed by this all-action, big-bucks extravaganza, but if you're looking for brain food, you'll need to find somewhere else to go for a nosh up.
>
> The story is simple. A computer programme magics up its own intelligence and turns against its programmers. Before long it is controlling every computer in the states and there's only one guy with the nous to stop it. So you don't need to be Einstein to work out the grand finale, but the effects and music are top notch. We gave it three Oz-stars out of five.

Q2   Poor punctuation has got this persuasive essay in a pickle. Rewrite it correcting the mistakes.

> _in the last twelve years the state of the promenade has worsened to the point of near dereliction if you walk along on any day you will see overflowing rubbish bins litter fast food wrappers and spat out chewing gum on the pavements how long are we going to accept this before we begin to change it_
>
> _it is my proposal that we as proud residents of the town begin to make a difference to our own environment I say we all need to set an example if you see someone dropping litter don't just shake your head in disgust and walk on stop pick up the rubbish and put it in the nearest bin if you know the person why not tell them that you are unhappy with their behaviour_
>
> _it won't do any harm to take a more active approach to looking after our town and it might just make things look a whole lot better_

Q3   Rewrite this extract adding some sophisticated punctuation
e.g. apostrophes, semi-colons and hyphens, where you see the underlines.

> The dry dust of the desert blew in through the open door_ it had drifted across the terracotta tiles_ long wisps of its sandy fingers reaching into the dark interior of Elianna's humble cottage.
>
> _ Mother. _
>
> A pitifully weak voice wandered through the body of the house_ a young voice, frightened and weary.
>
> But the voice would keep on calling_ it would get no response _ Elianna had left that morning and had no intention ever to return to the child or the house where she had lived all her life. Her child_s fate was now out of her hands_ Elianna_s decision was final.

Checking Practice

Q1   This local newspaper report needs some variety. Rewrite it, and liven up the language.

LOCAL GIRL NANCY COULD GET PICKED FOR THE COUNTY

Nancy Tucker, from the village of West Utheringstood, five miles outside Endville, came second at the East Crawlshire Draughts Trials on Sunday.

Nancy, 17, had everything to play for. Nancy said she was very nervous as she sat down to play her first game, but she was also nervous when she sat down to play the final game. She thinks she was more nervous for the final game than she was for the first game.

Nancy's Mum and Dad, Terry and Hilary, were both really pleased. "We are really pleased," said Terry. "Yes," said Hilary. Nancy was pipped to the post by last year's champion who comes from Busyton on the West side of the county. Nancy thinks she has proved that she is good enough to be picked for the County team.

The County team will be picked soon and announced next Thursday. The County team needs three players. Terry is confident that Nancy has done enough to get in. "I think she has done enough to get in this time," said Terry. "Yes," said Hilary. Nancy will go through to play for the county at the East of Britain trials in August if she gets picked. At seventeen, Nancy Tucker clearly has it all to play for.

Q2   Rewrite the dialogue from this play so that it sounds more like real speech.
You can change as many words as you want, but not the meanings.

Harold and Skipper are two old men who have known each other since they were in the army together during World War Two. They have allotments side by side in a plot on the outskirts of _____ (your town). This section of the play has them reminiscing about their return home from war.

HAROLD: *(sitting heavily on the upturned bucket)* I did not expect things to turn out the way they did.

SKIPPER: You should not have expected anything. The people who were not fighting had no concept of what life was really like for soldiers like ourselves.

HAROLD: *(pushing back his cap and scratching at his scalp)* But I *did* expect, Skipper. I expected flags waving and crowds cheering, exactly like there was when we left, do you remember?

SKIPPER: *(clenching his teeth)* Of course I remember. The train station was full of people who were staying safely at home. No wonder they were cheering.

HAROLD: You must not say that, Skip. Try not to be bitter.

SKIPPER: Why not? Why should I not?

HAROLD: It was a long time ago. It was almost fifty years ago, Skip.

SKIPPER: *(muttering)* Well it still feels like it was yesterday to me.

You gotter be cruel to be kind (sucking teeth)...

So ALL you have to do is sweat blood over writing your essay, and then sweat blood checking it.
I think I'll send the examiners some flowers to say thanks for being such great guys and gals.

Spoken Language Study

Q1   Which of these statements is true? Choose one answer.

  a)   Accents are only affected by regional factors.

  b)   Accents are variations in the words people use.

  c)   Accents are variations in pronunciation.

  d)   Accents are only affected by social factors.

Q2   Is Received Pronunciation a regional or social accent?

Q3   Give a definition of the following terms:

  a)   Dialect

  b)   Sociolect

  c)   Idiolect

  d)   Occupational sociolect

Q4   What factors can influence a speaker's idiolect?

Q5   Some people claim that men and women speak differently.
Give one example of a possible difference in the way men and women speak.

Q6   Why might a newsreader use informal language?

Q7   Describe two ways that scripted speech can be made to sound natural.

Spoken Language Study

Q1   The text below is a transcript of part of a radio show. Read it, then answer the questions.

a)   What's this?

b)   What's this an example of?

c)   What could you say about this word?

d)   What do you notice about the pauses in this transcript?

e)   What's this?

> RADIO PRESENTER:
>
> so (.) here we go (.) it's erm five past nine and you're listening to Radio Lingo FM (1) my name's Lionel Longton (.) and I'll be taking you all the way through to twelve o clock midday (.) playing you the very best hits around (1) but first the weather (1) well (.) erm (.) guess what (.) it's gonna be cold and rainy (1) nothing new there folks (1) after all (.) it is summer (.) so (.) let's think of ways to cheer ourselves up (1) here's an idea (.) why don't you take your grandmother to the shops (1) and see how much you get for her [*laughs*] (1) only joking all you grannies out there (1) my grandmother's eighty-nine and I love her (1) aren't grandmothers lovely (1) now, a few words of wisdom for you (1) he who drinks from the sea of lurve will never be thirsty (1) I like that (1) lurve (.) lurve (.) lurve (.) OK (.) enough frivolity (.)

In a transcript, pauses of less than a second are shown like this: (.). Longer pauses are shown by putting the number of seconds in brackets, like this: (2).

Q2   What is multi-modal talk?

Q3   Give two examples of texts that might contain multi-modal talk.

Q4   Pick out the examples of non-standard English in these sentences.

a) u coming later	c) no way m8	e) il come soon
b) @ my mums	d) shes like my bff	f) out wiv greg